CW00410540

2020

Published by Danilo Promotions Ltd., Unit 3, The io Centre, Lea Road, Waltham Abbey, EN9 1AS, England.

Printed in South Korea.

PERSONAL INFORMATION

NAME

ADDRESS

MOBILE

EMAIL

IN CASE OF EMERGENCY PLEASE CONTACT

NAME

ADDRESS

MOBILE

DOCTOR

DOCTOR TELEPHONE

KNOWN ALLERGIES

2020

JANUARY

WK	M	T	W	T	F	S	S
1			1	2	3	4	5
2	6	7	8	9	10	11	12
3	13	14	15	16	17	18	19
4	20	21	22	23	24	25	26
5	27	28	29	30	31		

FEBRUARY

WK	M	T	W	T	F	S	S
5						1	2
6	3	4	5	6	7	8	9
7	10	11	12	13	14	15	16
8	17	18	19	20	21	22	23
9	24	25	26	27	28	29	

MARCH

WK	M	T	W	T	F	S	S
9							1
10	2	3	4	5	6	7	8
11	9	10	11	12	13	14	15
12	16	17	18	19	20	21	22
13	23	24	25	26	27	28	29
14	30	31					

APRIL

WK	M	T	W	T	F	S	S
14			1	2	3	4	5
15	6	7	8	9	10	11	12
16	13	14	15	16	17	18	19
17	20	21	22	23	24	25	26
18	27	28	29	30			

MAY

WK	M	T	W	T	F	S	S
18					1	2	3
19	4	5	6	7	8	9	10
20	11	12	13	14	15	16	17
21	18	19	20	21	22	23	24
22	25	26	27	28	29	30	31

JUNE

WK	M	T	W	T	F	S	S
23	1	2	3	4	5	6	7
24	8	9	10	11	12	13	14
25	15	16	17	18	19	20	21
26	22	23	24	25	26	27	28
27	29	30					

JULY

WK	M	T	W	T	F	S	S
27			1	2	3	4	5
28	6	7	8	9	10	11	12
29	13	14	15	16	17	18	19
30	20	21	22	23	24	25	26
31	27	28	29	30	31		

AUGUST

WK	M	T	W	T	F	S	S
31						1	2
32	3	4	5	6	7	8	9
33	10	11	12	13	14	15	16
34	17	18	19	20	21	22	23
35	24	25	26	27	28	29	30
36	31						

SEPTEMBER

WK	M	T	W	T	F	S	S
36		1	2	3	4	5	6
37	7	8	9	10	11	12	13
38	14	15	16	17	18	19	20
39	21	22	23	24	25	26	27
40	28	29	30				

OCTOBER

WK	M	T	W	T	F	S	S
40				1	2	3	4
41	5	6	7	8	9	10	11
42	12	13	14	15	16	17	18
43	19	20	21	22	23	24	25
44	26	27	28	29	30	31	

NOVEMBER

WK	M	T	W	T	F	S	S
44							1
45	2	3	4	5	6	7	8
46	9	10	11	12	13	14	15
47	16	17	18	19	20	21	22
48	23	24	25	26	27	28	29
49	30						

DECEMBER

WK	M	T	W	T	F	S	S
49		1	2	3	4	5	6
50	7	8	9	10	11	12	13
51	14	15	16	17	18	19	20
52	21	22	23	24	25	26	27
53	28	29	30	31			

2020

NEW YEAR'S DAY	JANUARY 1
HOLIDAY (SCOTLAND)	JANUARY 2
CHINESE NEW YEAR (YEAR OF THE RAT)	JANUARY 25
ST. VALENTINE'S DAY	FEBRUARY 14
ASH WEDNESDAY	FEBRUARY 26
ST. DAVID'S DAY (WALES)	MARCH 1
WORLD BOOK DAY	MARCH 5
ST. PATRICK'S DAY (IRELAND)	MARCH 17
MOTHERING SUNDAY (UK)	MARCH 22
BRITISH SUMMER TIME BEGINS	MARCH 29
PASSOVER (PESACH) BEGINS	APRIL 8
GOOD FRIDAY (UK)	APRIL 10
EASTER SUNDAY	APRIL 12
EASTER MONDAY (UK & REPUBLIC OF IRELAND)	APRIL 13
ST. GEORGE'S DAY (ENGLAND)	APRIL 23
MAY DAY HOLIDAY (UK & REPUBLIC OF IRELAND)	MAY 4
SPRING BANK HOLIDAY (UK)	MAY 25
LONGEST DAY	JUNE 20
FATHER'S DAY	JUNE 21
HOLIDAY (NORTHERN IRELAND)	JULY 13
BANK HOLIDAY (SCOTLAND & REPUBLIC OF IRELAND)	AUGUST 3
AL-HIJRA BEGINS	AUGUST 19
SUMMER BANK HOLIDAY (ENG, NIR, WAL)	AUGUST 31
ROSH HASHANAH (JEWISH NEW YEAR) BEGINS	SEPTEMBER 18
THE UNITED NATIONS INTERNATIONAL DAY OF PEACE	SEPTEMBER 21
YOM KIPPUR (DAY OF ATONEMENT) BEGINS	SEPTEMBER 27
WORLD MENTAL HEALTH DAY	OCTOBER 10
BRITISH SUMMER TIME ENDS	OCTOBER 25
HOLIDAY (REPUBLIC OF IRELAND)	OCTOBER 26
HALLOWEEN	OCTOBER 31
GUY FAWKES NIGHT	NOVEMBER 5
REMEMBRANCE SUNDAY	NOVEMBER 8
DIWALI	NOVEMBER 14
ST. ANDREW'S DAY (SCOTLAND)	NOVEMBER 30
SHORTEST DAY	DECEMBER 21
CHRISTMAS DAY	DECEMBER 25
BOXING DAY (UK)	DECEMBER 26
ST. STEPHEN'S DAY (REPUBLIC OF IRELAND)	DECEMBER 26
BOXING DAY BANK HOLIDAY (UK)	DECEMBER 28
NEW YEAR'S EVE	DECEMBER 31

PLANNER 2020

JANUARY	FEBRUARY	MARCH
1 W	1 S	1 S
2 T	2 S	2 M
3 F	3 M	3 T
4 S	4 T	4 W
5 S	5 W	5 T
6 M	6 T	6 F
7 T	7 F	7 S
8 W	8 S	8 S
9 T	9 S	9 M
10 F	10 M	10 T
11 S	11 T	11 W
12 S	12 W	12 T
13 M	13 T	13 F
14 T	14 F	14 S
15 W	15 S	15 S
16 T	16 S	16 M
17 F	17 M	17 T
18 S	18 T	18 W
19 S	19 W	19 T
20 M	20 T	20 F
21 T	21 F	21 S
22 W	22 S	22 S
23 T	23 S	23 M
24 F	24 M	24 T
25 S	25 T	25 W
26 S	26 W	26 T
27 M	27 T	27 F
28 T	28 F	28 S
29 W	29 S	29 S
30 T		30 M
31 F		31 T

APRIL	MAY	JUNE
1 W	1 F	1 M
2 T	2 S	2 T
3 F	3 S	3 W
4 S	4 M	4 T
5 S	5 T	5 F
6 M	6 W	6 S
7 T	7 T	7 S
8 W	8 F	8 M
9 T	9 S	9 T
10 F	10 S	10 W
11 S	11 M	11 T
12 S	12 T	12 F
13 M	13 W	13 S
14 T	14 T	14 S
15 W	15 F	15 M
16 T	16 S	16 T
17 F	17 S	17 W
18 S	18 M	18 T
19 S	19 T	19 F
20 M	20 W	20 S
21 T	21 T	21 S
22 W	22 F	22 M
23 T	23 S	23 T
24 F	24 S	24 W
25 S	25 M	25 T
26 S	26 T	26 F
27 M	27 W	27 S
28 T	28 T	28 S
29 W	29 F	29 M
30 T	30 S	30 T
	31 S	

PLANNER 2020

JULY	AUGUST	SEPTEMBER
1 W	1 S	1 T
2 T	2 S	2 W
3 F	3 M	3 T
4 S	4 T	4 F
5 S	5 W	5 S
6 M	6 T	6 S
7 T	7 F	7 M
8 W	8 S	8 T
9 T	9 S	9 W
10 F	10 M	10 T
11 S	11 T	11 F
12 S	12 W	12 S
13 M	13 T	13 S
14 T	14 F	14 M
15 W	15 S	15 T
16 T	16 S	16 W
17 F	17 M	17 T
18 S	18 T	18 F
19 S	19 W	19 S
20 M	20 T	20 S
21 T	21 F	21 M
22 W	22 S	22 T
23 T	23 S	23 W
24 F	24 M	24 T
25 S	25 T	25 F
26 S	26 W	26 S
27 M	27 T	27 S
28 T	28 F	28 M
29 W	29 S	29 T
30 T	30 S	30 W
31 F	31 M	

OCTOBER

1 T
2 F
3 S
4 S
5 M
6 T
7 W
8 T
9 F
10 S
11 S
12 M
13 T
14 W
15 T
16 F
17 S
18 S
19 M
20 T
21 W
22 T
23 F
24 S
25 S
26 M
27 T
28 W
29 T
30 F
31 S

NOVEMBER

1 S
2 M
3 T
4 W
5 T
6 F
7 S
8 S
9 M
10 T
11 W
12 T
13 F
14 S
15 S
16 M
17 T
18 W
19 T
20 F
21 S
22 S
23 M
24 T
25 W
26 T
27 F
28 S
29 S
30 M

DECEMBER

1 T
2 W
3 T
4 F
5 S
6 S
7 M
8 T
9 W
10 T
11 F
12 S
13 S
14 M
15 T
16 W
17 T
18 F
19 S
20 S
21 M
22 T
23 W
24 T
25 F
26 S
27 S
28 M
29 T
30 W
31 T

WINGARDIUM LEVIOSA
SWISH & FLICK!

JANUARY

MY GOALS

SPECIAL DATES

NOTES

30 MONDAY

31 TUESDAY

NEW YEAR'S EV

1 WEDNESDAY

NEW YEAR'S DA

2 THURSDAY

HOLIDAY (SCOTLANI

FRIDAY 3

SATURDAY 4

SUNDAY 5

NOTES

M	T	W	T	F	S	S	M	T	W	T	F	S	S	M	T	W	T	F	S	S	M	T	W	T	F	S	S	M	T	W
16	17	18	19	20	21	22	23	24	25	26	27	28	29	30	31	1	2	3	4	5	6	7	8	9	10	11	12	13	14	15

6 MONDAY

7 TUESDAY

8 WEDNESDAY

9 THURSDAY

FRIDAY 10

SATURDAY 11

SUNDAY 12

OTES

W	T	F	S	S	M	T	W	T	F	S	S	M	T	W	T	F	S	S	M	T	W	T	F	S	S	M	T	W	T	F
1	2	3	4	5	6	7	8	9	10	11	12	13	14	15	16	17	18	19	20	21	22	23	24	25	26	27	28	29	30	31

13 MONDAY

14 TUESDAY

15 WEDNESDAY

16 THURSDAY

FRIDAY 17

SATURDAY 18

SUNDAY 19

OTES

V	T	F	S	S	M	T	W	T	F	S	S	M	T	W	T	F	S	S	M	T	W	T	F	S	S	M	T	W	T	F
1	2	3	4	5	6	7	8	9	10	11	12	13	14	15	16	17	18	19	20	21	22	23	24	25	26	27	28	29	30	31

20 MONDAY

21 TUESDAY

22 WEDNESDAY

23 THURSDAY

FRIDAY 24

HINESE NEW YEAR (YEAR OF THE RAT)

SATURDAY 25

SUNDAY 26

IOTES

W	T	F	S	S	M	T	W	T	F	S	S	M	T	W	T	F	S	S	M	T	W	T	F	S	S	M	T	W	T	F
1	2	3	4	5	6	7	8	9	10	11	12	13	14	15	16	17	18	19	20	21	22	23	24	25	26	27	28	29	30	31

DEDICATIO

HUFFLEPUFF

PATIENCE

LOYALTY

FEBRUARY

MY GOALS

SPECIAL DATES

NOTES

27 MONDAY

28 TUESDAY

29 WEDNESDAY

30 THURSDAY

FRIDAY 31

SATURDAY 1

SUNDAY 2

NOTES

T	F	S	S	M	T	W	T	F	S	S	M	T	W	T	F	S	S	M	T	W	T	F	S	S	M	T	W	T	F	S
16	17	18	19	20	21	22	23	24	25	26	27	28	29	30	31	1	2	3	4	5	6	7	8	9	10	11	12	13	14	15

F

3 MONDAY

4 TUESDAY

5 WEDNESDAY

6 THURSDAY

FRIDAY 7

SATURDAY 8

SUNDAY 9

NOTES

S	S	M	T	W	T	F	S	S	M	T	W	T	F	S	S	M	T	W	T	F	S	S	M	T	W	T	F	S
1	2	3	4	5	6	7	8	9	10	11	12	13	14	15	16	17	18	19	20	21	22	23	24	25	26	27	28	29

10 MONDAY

11 TUESDAY

12 WEDNESDAY

13 THURSDAY

ST. VALENTINE'S DAY

FRIDAY 14

SATURDAY 15

SUNDAY 16

NOTES

S	S	M	T	W	T	F	S	S	M	T	W	T	F	S	S	M	T	W	T	F	S	S	M	T	W	T	F	S
1	2	3	4	5	6	7	8	9	10	11	12	13	14	15	16	17	18	19	20	21	22	23	24	25	26	27	28	29

17 MONDAY

18 TUESDAY

19 WEDNESDAY

20 THURSDAY

FRIDAY **21**

SATURDAY **22**

SUNDAY **23**

NOTES

S	S	M	T	W	T	F	S	S	M	T	W	T	F	S	S	M	T	W	T	F	S	S	M	T	W	T	F	S
1	2	3	4	5	6	7	8	9	10	11	12	13	14	15	16	17	18	19	20	21	22	23	24	25	26	27	28	29

FREE
THE HOUSE-
ELVES

MARCH

MY GOALS

SPECIAL DATES

NOTES

24 MONDAY

25 TUESDAY

26 WEDNESDAY

ASH WEDNESDA

27 THURSDAY

FRIDAY **28**

SATURDAY **29**

T. DAVID'S DAY (WALES)

SUNDAY **1**

OTES

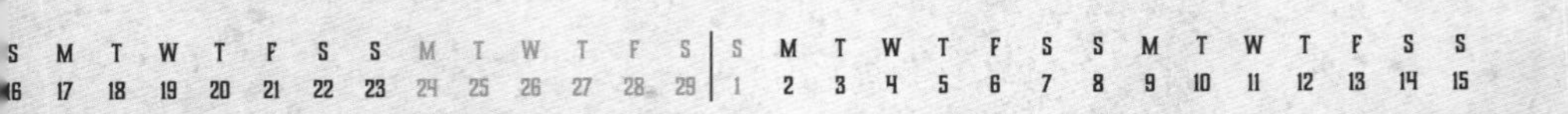

M

2 MONDAY

3 TUESDAY

4 WEDNESDAY

5 THURSDAY

WORLD BOOK DA

FRIDAY 6

SATURDAY 7

SUNDAY 8

OTES

S	M	T	W	T	F	S	S	M	T	W	T	F	S	S	M	T	W	T	F	S	S	M	T	W	T	F	S	S	M	T
	2	3	4	5	6	7	8	9	10	11	12	13	14	15	16	17	18	19	20	21	22	23	24	25	26	27	28	29	30	31

9 MONDAY

10 TUESDAY

11 WEDNESDAY

12 THURSDAY

FRIDAY 13

SATURDAY 14

SUNDAY 15

NOTES

S	M	T	W	T	F	S	S	M	T	W	T	F	S	S	M	T	W	T	F	S	S	M	T	W	T	F	S	S	M	T
1	2	3	4	5	6	7	8	9	10	11	12	13	14	15	16	17	18	19	20	21	22	23	24	25	26	27	28	29	30	31

M

16 MONDAY

17 TUESDAY

ST. PATRICK'S DAY (IRELAND)

18 WEDNESDAY

19 THURSDAY

FRIDAY **20**

SATURDAY **21**

MOTHERING SUNDAY (UK)

SUNDAY **22**

NOTES

S	M	T	W	T	F	S	S	M	T	W	T	F	S	S	M	T	W	T	F	S	S	M	T	W	T	F	S	S	M	T
1	2	3	4	5	6	7	8	9	10	11	12	13	14	15	16	17	18	19	20	21	22	23	24	25	26	27	28	29	30	31

23 MONDAY

24 TUESDAY

25 WEDNESDAY

26 THURSDAY

FRIDAY 27

SATURDAY 28

SUNDAY 29

RITISH SUMMER TIME BEGINS

OTES

S	M	T	W	T	F	S	S	M	T	W	T	F	S	S	M	T	W	T	F	S	S	M	T	W	T	F	S	S	M	T
1	2	3	4	5	6	7	8	9	10	11	12	13	14	15	16	17	18	19	20	21	22	23	24	25	26	27	28	29	30	31

PRIDE

AMBITION

CUNNING

SLYTHERIN

APRIL

MY GOALS

SPECIAL DATES

NOTES

30 MONDAY

31 TUESDAY

1 WEDNESDAY

2 THURSDAY

FRIDAY 3

SATURDAY 4

SUNDAY 5

OTES

M	T	W	T	F	S	S	M	T	W	T	F	S	S	M	T	W	T	F	S	S	M	T	W	T	F	S	S	M	T	W
6	17	18	19	20	21	22	23	24	25	26	27	28	29	30	31	1	2	3	4	5	6	7	8	9	10	11	12	13	14	15

6 MONDAY

7 TUESDAY

8 WEDNESDAY

PASSOVER (PESACH) BEGIN

9 THURSDAY

OD FRIDAY (UK) FRIDAY 10

SATURDAY 11

ASTER SUNDAY SUNDAY 12

OTES

W	T	F	S	S	M	T	W	T	F	S	S	M	T	W	T	F	S	S	M	T	W	T	F	S	S	M	T	W	T
1	2	3	4	5	6	7	8	9	10	11	12	13	14	15	16	17	18	19	20	21	22	23	24	25	26	27	28	29	30

13 MONDAY EASTER MONDAY (UK & REPUBLIC OF IRELAN

14 TUESDAY

15 WEDNESDAY

16 THURSDAY

FRIDAY 17

SATURDAY 18

SUNDAY 19

NOTES

W	T	F	S	S	M	T	W	T	F	S	S	M	T	W	T	F	S	S	M	T	W	T	F	S	S	M	T	W	T
1	2	3	4	5	6	7	8	9	10	11	12	13	14	15	16	17	18	19	20	21	22	23	24	25	26	27	28	29	30

20 MONDAY

21 TUESDAY

22 WEDNESDAY

23 THURSDAY

ST. GEORGE'S DAY (ENGLAND

APRIL 2020

FRIDAY 24

SATURDAY 25

SUNDAY 26

OTES

W	T	F	S	S	M	T	W	T	F	S	S	M	T	W	T	F	S	S	M	T	W	T	F	S	S	M	T	W	T
1	2	3	4	5	6	7	8	9	10	11	12	13	14	15	16	17	18	19	20	21	22	23	24	25	26	27	28	29	30

MOONY,
WORMTAIL,
PADFOOT & PRONGS

ARE PROUD TO PRESENT

HOGWARTS

The
MARAUDER'S
MAP

ITINERARIUM MARAUDENTIUM

MAY

MY GOALS

SPECIAL DATES

NOTES

27 MONDAY

28 TUESDAY

29 WEDNESDAY

30 THURSDAY

FRIDAY 1

SATURDAY 2

SUNDAY 3

NOTES

T	F	S	S	M	T	W	T	F	S	S	M	T	W	T	F	S	S	M	T	W	T	F	S	S	M	T	W	T	F	S
16	17	18	19	20	21	22	23	24	25	26	27	28	29	30	1	2	3	4	5	6	7	8	9	10	11	12	13	14	15	16

4 MONDAY

MAY DAY HOLIDAY (UK & REPUBLIC OF IRELAND)

5 TUESDAY

6 WEDNESDAY

7 THURSDAY

FRIDAY 8

SATURDAY 9

SUNDAY 10

NOTES

F	S	S	M	T	W	T	F	S	S	M	T	W	T	F	S	S	M	T	W	T	F	S	S	M	T	W	T	F	S	S
1	2	3	4	5	6	7	8	9	10	11	12	13	14	15	16	17	18	19	20	21	22	23	24	25	26	27	28	29	30	31

11 MONDAY

12 TUESDAY

13 WEDNESDAY

14 THURSDAY

FRIDAY 15

SATURDAY 16

M

SUNDAY 17

OTES

F	S	S	M	T	W	T	F	S	S	M	T	W	T	F	S	S	M	T	W	T	F	S	S	M	T	W	T	F	S	S
1	2	3	4	5	6	7	8	9	10	11	12	13	14	15	16	17	18	19	20	21	22	23	24	25	26	27	28	29	30	31

18 MONDAY

19 TUESDAY

20 WEDNESDAY

21 THURSDAY

FRIDAY 22

SATURDAY 23

M

SUNDAY 24

OTES

S	S	M	T	W	T	F	S	S	M	T	W	T	F	S	S	M	T	W	T	F	S	S	M	T	W	T	F	S	S
2	3	4	5	6	7	8	9	10	11	12	13	14	15	16	17	18	19	20	21	22	23	24	25	26	27	28	29	30	31

25 MONDAY SPRING BANK HOLIDAY (UK

26 TUESDAY

27 WEDNESDAY

28 THURSDAY

FRIDAY 29

SATURDAY 30

SUNDAY 31

OTES

S	S	M	T	W	T	F	S	S	M	T	W	T	F	S	S	M	T	W	T	F	S	S	M	T	W	T	F	S	S
2	3	4	5	6	7	8	9	10	11	12	13	14	15	16	17	18	19	20	21	22	23	24	25	26	27	28	29	30	31

DOBBY

FREE

JUNE

MY GOALS

SPECIAL DATES

NOTES

1 MONDAY

2 TUESDAY

3 WEDNESDAY

4 THURSDAY

FRIDAY 5

SATURDAY 6

SUNDAY 7

NOTES

M	T	W	T	F	S	S	M	T	W	T	F	S	S	M	T	W	T	F	S	S	M	T	W	T	F	S	S	M	T
1	2	3	4	5	6	7	8	9	10	11	12	13	14	15	16	17	18	19	20	21	22	23	24	25	26	27	28	29	30

J

8 MONDAY

9 TUESDAY

10 WEDNESDAY

11 THURSDAY

FRIDAY 12

SATURDAY 13

SUNDAY 14

NOTES

M	T	W	T	F	S	S	M	T	W	T	F	S	S	M	T	W	T	F	S	S	M	T	W	T	F	S	S	M	T
1	2	3	4	5	6	7	8	9	10	11	12	13	14	15	16	17	18	19	20	21	22	23	24	25	26	27	28	29	30

J

15 MONDAY

16 TUESDAY

17 WEDNESDAY

18 THURSDAY

FRIDAY 19

LONGEST DAY

SATURDAY 20

FATHER'S DAY

SUNDAY 21

NOTES

M	T	W	T	F	S	S	M	T	W	T	F	S	S	M	T	W	T	F	S	S	M	T	W	T	F	S	S	M	T
1	2	3	4	5	6	7	8	9	10	11	12	13	14	15	16	17	18	19	20	21	22	23	24	25	26	27	28	29	30

22 MONDAY

23 TUESDAY

24 WEDNESDAY

25 THURSDAY

FRIDAY 26

SATURDAY 27

SUNDAY 28

NOTES

M	T	W	T	F	S	S	M	T	W	T	F	S	S	M	T	W	T	F	S	S	M	T	W	T	F	S	S	M	T
1	2	3	4	5	6	7	8	9	10	11	12	13	14	15	16	17	18	19	20	21	22	23	24	25	26	27	28	29	30

BRAVERY

GRYFFINDOR

COURAGE

DETERMINATION

JULY

MY GOALS

SPECIAL DATES

NOTES

29 MONDAY

30 TUESDAY

1 WEDNESDAY

2 THURSDAY

FRIDAY **3**

SATURDAY **4**

SUNDAY **5**

OTES

J

W	T	F	S	S	M	T	W	T	F	S	S	M	T	W	T	F	S	S	M	T	W	T	F	S	S	M	T	W	T
17	18	19	20	21	22	23	24	25	26	27	28	29	30	1	2	3	4	5	6	7	8	9	10	11	12	13	14	15	16

6 MONDAY

7 TUESDAY

8 WEDNESDAY

9 THURSDAY

FRIDAY 10

SATURDAY 11

SUNDAY 12

TES

T	F	S	S	M	T	W	T	F	S	S	M	T	W	T	F	S	S	M	T	W	T	F	S	S	M	T	W	T	F
2	3	4	5	6	7	8	9	10	11	12	13	14	15	16	17	18	19	20	21	22	23	24	25	26	27	28	29	30	31

J

13 MONDAY HOLIDAY (NORTHERN IRELAN

14 TUESDAY

15 WEDNESDAY

16 THURSDAY

FRIDAY 17

SATURDAY 18

SUNDAY 19

OTES

W	T	F	S	S	M	T	W	T	F	S	S	M	T	W	T	F	S	S	M	T	W	T	F	S	S	M	T	W	T	F
1	2	3	4	5	6	7	8	9	10	11	12	13	14	15	16	17	18	19	20	21	22	23	24	25	26	27	28	29	30	31

20 MONDAY

21 TUESDAY

22 WEDNESDAY

23 THURSDAY

FRIDAY 24

SATURDAY 25

SUNDAY 26

NOTES

W	T	F	S	S	M	T	W	T	F	S	S	M	T	W	T	F	S	S	M	T	W	T	F	S	S	M	T	W	T	F
1	2	3	4	5	6	7	8	9	10	11	12	13	14	15	16	17	18	19	20	21	22	23	24	25	26	27	28	29	30	31

LUMOS
MAXIMA
a light creation spell, used to illuminate the tip of the caster's wand

AUGUST

MY GOALS

SPECIAL DATES

NOTES

27 MONDAY

28 TUESDAY

29 WEDNESDAY

30 THURSDAY

FRIDAY **31**

SATURDAY **1**

SUNDAY **2**

A

NOTES

T	F	S	S	M	T	W	T	F	S	S	M	T	W	T	F	S	S	M	T	W	T	F	S	S	M	T	W	T	F	S
16	17	18	19	20	21	22	23	24	25	26	27	28	29	30	31	1	2	3	4	5	6	7	8	9	10	11	12	13	14	15

3 MONDAY

BANK HOLIDAY (SCOTLAND & REPUBLIC OF IRELAND)

4 TUESDAY

5 WEDNESDAY

6 THURSDAY

FRIDAY 7

SATURDAY 8

SUNDAY 9

A

NOTES

HP™

S	S	M	T	W	T	F	S	S	M	T	W	T	F	S	S	M	T	W	T	F	S	S	M	T	W	T	F	S	S	M
1	2	3	4	5	6	7	8	9	10	11	12	13	14	15	16	17	18	19	20	21	22	23	24	25	26	27	28	29	30	31

10 MONDAY

11 TUESDAY

12 WEDNESDAY

13 THURSDAY

FRIDAY 14

SATURDAY 15

SUNDAY 16

A

NOTES

S	S	M	T	W	T	F	S	S	M	T	W	T	F	S	S	M	T	W	T	F	S	S	M	T	W	T	F	S	S	M
1	2	3	4	5	6	7	8	9	10	11	12	13	14	15	16	17	18	19	20	21	22	23	24	25	26	27	28	29	30	31

17 MONDAY

18 TUESDAY

19 WEDNESDAY

AL-HIJRA BEGIN

20 THURSDAY

FRIDAY 21

SATURDAY 22

SUNDAY 23

A

OTES

S	M	T	W	T	F	S	S	M	T	W	T	F	S	S	M	T	W	T	F	S	S	M	T	W	T	F	S	S	M
2	3	4	5	6	7	8	9	10	11	12	13	14	15	16	17	18	19	20	21	22	23	24	25	26	27	28	29	30	31

24 MONDAY

25 TUESDAY

26 WEDNESDAY

27 THURSDAY

FRIDAY 28

SATURDAY 29

SUNDAY 30

A

OTES

S	M	T	W	T	F	S	S	M	T	W	T	F	S	S	M	T	W	T	F	S	S	M	T	W	T	F	S	S	M
2	3	4	5	6	7	8	9	10	11	12	13	14	15	16	17	18	19	20	21	22	23	24	25	26	27	28	29	30	31

Dobby
HAS NO MASTER
DOBBY
IS A FREE ELF

SEPTEMBER

MY GOALS

SPECIAL DATES

NOTES

31 MONDAY SUMMER BANK HOLIDAY (ENG, NIR, WA

1 TUESDAY

2 WEDNESDAY

3 THURSDAY

FRIDAY 4

SATURDAY 5

SUNDAY 6

OTES

M	T	W	T	F	S	S	M	T	W	T	F	S	S	M	T	W	T	F	S	S	M	T	W	T	F	S	S	M	T
17	18	19	20	21	22	23	24	25	26	27	28	29	30	31	1	2	3	4	5	6	7	8	9	10	11	12	13	14	15

7 MONDAY

8 TUESDAY

9 WEDNESDAY

10 THURSDAY

FRIDAY 11

SATURDAY 12

SUNDAY 13

S

NOTES

T	W	T	F	S	S	M	T	W	T	F	S	S	M	T	W	T	F	S	S	M	T	W	T	F	S	S	M	T	W
1	2	3	4	5	6	7	8	9	10	11	12	13	14	15	16	17	18	19	20	21	22	23	24	25	26	27	28	29	30

14 MONDAY

15 TUESDAY

16 WEDNESDAY

17 THURSDAY

ROSH HASHANAH (JEWISH NEW YEAR) BEGINS

FRIDAY 18

SATURDAY 19

SUNDAY 20

NOTES

T	W	T	F	S	S	M	T	W	T	F	S	S	M	T	W	T	F	S	S	M	T	W	T	F	S	S	M	T	W
1	2	3	4	5	6	7	8	9	10	11	12	13	14	15	16	17	18	19	20	21	22	23	24	25	26	27	28	29	30

21 MONDAY

THE UNITED NATIONS INTERNATIONAL DAY OF PEACE

22 TUESDAY

23 WEDNESDAY

24 THURSDAY

FRIDAY 25

SATURDAY 26

YOM KIPPUR (DAY OF ATONEMENT) BEGINS

SUNDAY 27

NOTES

T	W	T	F	S	S	M	T	W	T	F	S	S	M	T	W	T	F	S	S	M	T	W	T	F	S	S	M	T	W
1	2	3	4	5	6	7	8	9	10	11	12	13	14	15	16	17	18	19	20	21	22	23	24	25	26	27	28	29	30

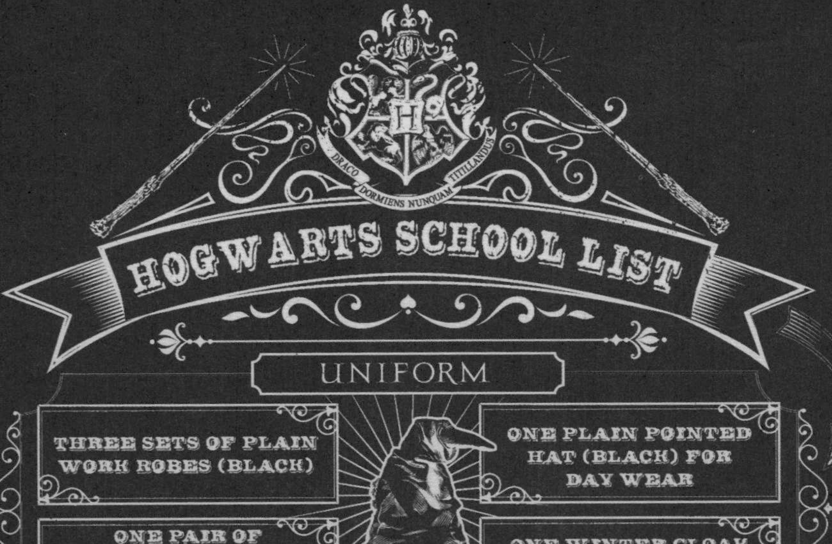

HOGWARTS SCHOOL LIST

UNIFORM

THREE SETS OF PLAIN WORK ROBES (BLACK)

ONE PLAIN POINTED HAT (BLACK) FOR DAY WEAR

ONE PAIR OF PROTECTIVE GLOVES (DRAGON HIDE OR SIMILAR)

ONE WINTER CLOAK (BLACK, SILVER FASTENINGS)

PLEASE NOTE THAT ALL PUPILS' CLOTHES SHOULD CARRY NAME TAGS.

BOOK LIST

THE STANDARD BOOK OF SPELLS (GRADE 1) BY MIRANDA GOSHAWK

ONE THOUSAND MAGICAL HERBS AND FUNGI BY PHYLLIDA SPORE

A HISTORY OF MAGIC BY BATHILDA BAGSHOT

MAGICAL DRAFTS AND POTIONS BY ARSENIUS JIGGER

MAGICAL THEORY BY ADALBERT WAFFLING

FANTASTIC BEASTS AND WHERE TO FIND THEM BY NEWT SCAMANDER

A BEGINNER'S GUIDE TO TRANSFIGURATION BY EMERIC SWITCH

THE DARK FORCES: A GUIDE TO SELF-PROTECTION BY QUENTIN TRIMBLE

OTHER EQUIPMENT

1 wand

1 telescope

1 cauldron (pewter, standard size 2)

1 set brass scales

1 set glass or crystal phials

Students may also bring an Owl or a Cat or a Toad.

PARENTS ARE REMINDED THAT FIRST-YEARS ARE NOT ALLOWED THEIR OWN BROOMSTICKS.

FIRST YEAR

OCTOBER

MY GOALS

SPECIAL DATES

NOTES

28 MONDAY

29 TUESDAY

30 WEDNESDAY

1 THURSDAY

FRIDAY 2

SATURDAY 3

SUNDAY 4

OTES

W	T	F	S	S	M	T	W	T	F	S	S	M	T	W	T	F	S	S	M	T	W	T	F	S	S	M	T	W	T
16	17	18	19	20	21	22	23	24	25	26	27	28	29	30	1	2	3	4	5	6	7	8	9	10	11	12	13	14	15

5 MONDAY

6 TUESDAY

7 WEDNESDAY

8 THURSDAY

FRIDAY 9

ORLD MENTAL HEALTH DAY

SATURDAY 10

SUNDAY 11

TES

F	S	S	M	T	W	T	F	S	S	M	T	W	T	F	S	S	M	T	W	T	F	S	S	M	T	W	T	F	S
2	3	4	5	6	7	8	9	10	11	12	13	14	15	16	17	18	19	20	21	22	23	24	25	26	27	28	29	30	31

12 MONDAY

13 TUESDAY

14 WEDNESDAY

15 THURSDAY

FRIDAY 16

SATURDAY 17

SUNDAY 18

OTES

F	S	S	M	T	W	T	F	S	S	M	T	W	T	F	S	S	M	T	W	T	F	S	S	M	T	W	T	F	S
2	3	4	5	6	7	8	9	10	11	12	13	14	15	16	17	18	19	20	21	22	23	24	25	26	27	28	29	30	31

19 MONDAY

20 TUESDAY

21 WEDNESDAY

22 THURSDAY

FRIDAY 23

SATURDAY 24

SUNDAY 25

RITISH SUMMER TIME ENDS

NOTES

T	F	S	S	M	T	W	T	F	S	S	M	T	W	T	F	S	S	M	T	W	T	F	S	S	M	T	W	T	F	S
1	2	3	4	5	6	7	8	9	10	11	12	13	14	15	16	17	18	19	20	21	22	23	24	25	26	27	28	29	30	31

O

WIT

WISDOM

LEARNING

RAVENCLAW

NOVEMBER

MY GOALS

SPECIAL DATES

NOTES

26 MONDAY

HOLIDAY (REPUBLIC OF IRELAND)

27 TUESDAY

28 WEDNESDAY

29 THURSDAY

FRIDAY 30

HALLOWEEN

SATURDAY 31

SUNDAY 1

N

NOTES

HP™

F	S	S	M	T	W	T	F	S	S	M	T	W	T	F	S	S	M	T	W	T	F	S	S	M	T	W	T	F	S	S
16	17	18	19	20	21	22	23	24	25	26	27	28	29	30	31	1	2	3	4	5	6	7	8	9	10	11	12	13	14	15

2 MONDAY

3 TUESDAY

4 WEDNESDAY

5 THURSDAY GUY FAWKES NIGH

FRIDAY 6

SATURDAY 7

REMEMBRANCE SUNDAY

SUNDAY 8

NOTES

S	M	T	W	T	F	S	S	M	T	W	T	F	S	S	M	T	W	T	F	S	S	M	T	W	T	F	S	S	M
1	2	3	4	5	6	7	8	9	10	11	12	13	14	15	16	17	18	19	20	21	22	23	24	25	26	27	28	29	30

9 MONDAY

10 TUESDAY

11 WEDNESDAY

12 THURSDAY

FRIDAY 13

IWALI

SATURDAY 14

SUNDAY 15

IOTES

S	M	T	W	T	F	S	S	M	T	W	T	F	S	S	M	T	W	T	F	S	S	M	T	W	T	F	S	S	M
1	2	3	4	5	6	7	8	9	10	11	12	13	14	15	16	17	18	19	20	21	22	23	24	25	26	27	28	29	30

16 MONDAY

17 TUESDAY

18 WEDNESDAY

19 THURSDAY

FRIDAY 20

SATURDAY 21

SUNDAY 22

OTES

N

S	M	T	W	T	F	S	S	M	T	W	T	F	S	S	M	T	W	T	F	S	S	M	T	W	T	F	S	S	M
1	2	3	4	5	6	7	8	9	10	11	12	13	14	15	16	17	18	19	20	21	22	23	24	25	26	27	28	29	30

23 MONDAY

24 TUESDAY

25 WEDNESDAY

26 THURSDAY

FRIDAY 27

SATURDAY 28

SUNDAY 29

OTES

S	M	T	W	T	F	S	S	M	T	W	T	F	S	S	M	T	W	T	F	S	S	M	T	W	T	F	S	S	M
1	2	3	4	5	6	7	8	9	10	11	12	13	14	15	16	17	18	19	20	21	22	23	24	25	26	27	28	29	30

N

HARRY POTTER!
SO LONG IT'S BEEN.

DECEMBER

MY GOALS

SPECIAL DATES

NOTES

30 MONDAY

ST. ANDREW'S DAY (SCOTLAN

1 TUESDAY

2 WEDNESDAY

3 THURSDAY

FRIDAY 4

SATURDAY 5

SUNDAY 6

OTES

M	T	W	T	F	S	S	M	T	W	T	F	S	S	M	T	W	T	F	S	S	M	T	W	T	F	S	S	M
16	17	18	19	20	21	22	23	24	25	26	27	28	29	30	1	2	3	4	5	6	7	8	9	10	11	12	13	14

7 MONDAY

8 TUESDAY

9 WEDNESDAY

10 THURSDAY

FRIDAY 11

SATURDAY 12

SUNDAY 13

OTES

T	W	T	F	S	S	M	T	W	T	F	S	S	M	T	W	T	F	S	S	M	T	W	T	F	S	S	M	T	W	T
1	2	3	4	5	6	7	8	9	10	11	12	13	14	15	16	17	18	19	20	21	22	23	24	25	26	27	28	29	30	31

Hp™

D

14 MONDAY

15 TUESDAY

16 WEDNESDAY

17 THURSDAY

FRIDAY 18

SATURDAY 19

SUNDAY 20

OTES

D

W	T	F	S	S	M	T	W	T	F	S	S	M	T	W	T	F	S	S	M	T	W	T	F	S	S	M	T	W	T
2	3	4	5	6	7	8	9	10	11	12	13	14	15	16	17	18	19	20	21	22	23	24	25	26	27	28	29	30	31

21 MONDAY

SHORTEST DAY

22 TUESDAY

23 WEDNESDAY

24 THURSDAY

RISTMAS DAY

FRIDAY 25

XING DAY (UK) / ST. STEPHEN'S DAY (REPUBLIC OF IRELAND)

SATURDAY 26

SUNDAY 27

OTES

HP™

D

T	W	T	F	S	S	M	T	W	T	F	S	S	M	T	W	T	F	S	S	M	T	W	T	F	S	S	M	T	W	T
	2	3	4	5	6	7	8	9	10	11	12	13	14	15	16	17	18	19	20	21	22	23	24	25	26	27	28	29	30	31

28 MONDAY BOXING DAY BANK HOLIDAY (UK)

29 TUESDAY

30 WEDNESDAY

31 THURSDAY NEW YEAR'S EVE

NEW YEAR'S DAY

FRIDAY 1

SATURDAY 2

SUNDAY 3

NOTES

W	T	F	S	S	M	T	W	T	F	S	S	M	T	W	T	F	S	S	M	T	W	T	F	S	S	M	T	W	T	F
16	17	18	19	20	21	22	23	24	25	26	27	28	29	30	31	1	2	3	4	5	6	7	8	9	10	11	12	13	14	15

PLANNER 2021

JANUARY	FEBRUARY	MARCH
1 F	1 M	1 M
2 S	2 T	2 T
3 S	3 W	3 W
4 M	4 T	4 T
5 T	5 F	5 F
6 W	6 S	6 S
7 T	7 S	7 S
8 F	8 M	8 M
9 S	9 T	9 T
10 S	10 W	10 W
11 M	11 T	11 T
12 T	12 F	12 F
13 W	13 S	13 S
14 T	14 S	14 S
15 F	15 M	15 M
16 S	16 T	16 T
17 S	17 W	17 W
18 M	18 T	18 T
19 T	19 F	19 F
20 W	20 S	20 S
21 T	21 S	21 S
22 F	22 M	22 M
23 S	23 T	23 T
24 S	24 W	24 W
25 M	25 T	25 T
26 T	26 F	26 F
27 W	27 S	27 S
28 T	28 S	28 S
29 F		29 M
30 S		30 T
31 S		31 W

APRIL	MAY	JUNE
1 T	1 S	1 T
2 F	2 S	2 W
3 S	3 M	3 T
4 S	4 T	4 F
5 M	5 W	5 S
6 T	6 T	6 S
7 W	7 F	7 M
8 T	8 S	8 T
9 F	9 S	9 W
0 S	10 M	10 T
11 S	11 T	11 F
2 M	12 W	12 S
3 T	13 T	13 S
4 W	14 F	14 M
5 T	15 S	15 T
6 F	16 S	16 W
7 S	17 M	17 T
8 S	18 T	18 F
9 M	19 W	19 S
0 T	20 T	20 S
21 W	21 F	21 M
2 T	22 S	22 T
3 F	23 S	23 W
4 S	24 M	24 T
5 S	25 T	25 F
6 M	26 W	26 S
7 T	27 T	27 S
8 W	28 F	28 M
9 T	29 S	29 T
0 F	30 S	30 W
	31 M	

PLANNER 2021

JULY	AUGUST	SEPTEMBER
1 T	1 S	1 W
2 F	2 M	2 T
3 S	3 T	3 F
4 S	4 W	4 S
5 M	5 T	5 S
6 T	6 F	6 M
7 W	7 S	7 T
8 T	8 S	8 W
9 F	9 M	9 T
10 S	10 T	10 F
11 S	11 W	11 S
12 M	12 T	12 S
13 T	13 F	13 M
14 W	14 S	14 T
15 T	15 S	15 W
16 F	16 M	16 T
17 S	17 T	17 F
18 S	18 W	18 S
19 M	19 T	19 S
20 T	20 F	20 M
21 W	21 S	21 T
22 T	22 S	22 W
23 F	23 M	23 T
24 S	24 T	24 F
25 S	25 W	25 S
26 M	26 T	26 S
27 T	27 F	27 M
28 W	28 S	28 T
29 T	29 S	29 W
30 F	30 M	30 T
31 S	31 T	

OCTOBER	NOVEMBER	DECEMBER
1 F	1 M	1 W
2 S	2 T	2 T
3 S	3 W	3 F
4 M	4 T	4 S
5 T	5 F	5 S
6 W	6 S	6 M
7 T	7 S	7 T
8 F	8 M	8 W
9 S	9 T	9 T
10 S	10 W	10 F
11 M	11 T	11 S
12 T	12 F	12 S
13 W	13 S	13 M
14 T	14 S	14 T
15 F	15 M	15 W
16 S	16 T	16 T
17 S	17 W	17 F
18 M	18 T	18 S
19 T	19 F	19 S
20 W	20 S	20 M
21 T	21 S	21 T
22 F	22 M	22 W
23 S	23 T	23 T
24 S	24 W	24 F
25 M	25 T	25 S
26 T	26 F	26 S
27 W	27 S	27 M
28 T	28 S	28 T
29 F	29 M	29 W
30 S	30 T	30 T
31 S		31 F

2021

JANUARY

WK	M	T	W	T	F	S	S
53					1	2	3
1	4	5	6	7	8	9	10
2	11	12	13	14	15	16	17
3	18	19	20	21	22	23	24
4	25	26	27	28	29	30	31

FEBRUARY

WK	M	T	W	T	F	S	S
5	1	2	3	4	5	6	7
6	8	9	10	11	12	13	14
7	15	16	17	18	19	20	21
8	22	23	24	25	26	27	28

MARCH

WK	M	T	W	T	F	S	S
9	1	2	3	4	5	6	7
10	8	9	10	11	12	13	14
11	15	16	17	18	19	20	21
12	22	23	24	25	26	27	28
13	29	30	31				

APRIL

WK	M	T	W	T	F	S	S
13				1	2	3	4
14	5	6	7	8	9	10	11
15	12	13	14	15	16	17	18
16	19	20	21	22	23	24	25
17	26	27	28	29	30		

MAY

WK	M	T	W	T	F	S	S
17						1	2
18	3	4	5	6	7	8	9
19	10	11	12	13	14	15	16
20	17	18	19	20	21	22	23
21	24	25	26	27	28	29	30
22	31						

JUNE

WK	M	T	W	T	F	S	S
22		1	2	3	4	5	6
23	7	8	9	10	11	12	13
24	14	15	16	17	18	19	20
25	21	22	23	24	25	26	27
26	28	29	30				

JULY

WK	M	T	W	T	F	S	S
26				1	2	3	4
27	5	6	7	8	9	10	11
28	12	13	14	15	16	17	18
29	19	20	21	22	23	24	25
30	26	27	28	29	30	31	

AUGUST

WK	M	T	W	T	F	S	S
30							1
31	2	3	4	5	6	7	8
32	9	10	11	12	13	14	15
33	16	17	18	19	20	21	22
34	23	24	25	26	27	28	29
35	30	31					

SEPTEMBER

WK	M	T	W	T	F	S	S
35			1	2	3	4	5
36	6	7	8	9	10	11	12
37	13	14	15	16	17	18	19
38	20	21	22	23	24	25	26
39	27	28	29	30			

OCTOBER

WK	M	T	W	T	F	S	S
39					1	2	3
40	4	5	6	7	8	9	10
41	11	12	13	14	15	16	17
42	18	19	20	21	22	23	24
43	25	26	27	28	29	30	31

NOVEMBER

WK	M	T	W	T	F	S	S
44	1	2	3	4	5	6	7
45	8	9	10	11	12	13	14
46	15	16	17	18	19	20	21
47	22	23	24	25	26	27	28
48	29	30					

DECEMBER

WK	M	T	W	T	F	S	S
48			1	2	3	4	5
49	6	7	8	9	10	11	12
50	13	14	15	16	17	18	19
51	20	21	22	23	24	25	26
52	27	28	29	30	31